SCRIBBLE YOUR PEN

(MAKE SURE IT WORKS)

YOUR NAME:

_____

FUCK OFF, I MEAN GOOD MORNING

HAVEN'T FOUND A WAY TO SAY "FUCK YOU" POLITELY

WELL, FUUUUUUUCK

EVIL FUCKING TWINS (NOT US)

C'EST LA FUCKING VIE

WE'LL BE FRIENDS FOREVER BECAUSE YOU KNOW TOO FUCKING MUCH

WE'D LOVE TO GET FUCKED BY SOMEONE OTHER THAN LIFE

SURROUND YOURSELF WITH MARTINIS NOT FUCKS

I'M CONFIDENT MY LAST WORDS WILL BE "ARE YOU FUCKING KIDDING ME?"

How to find happiness:

Read. Write. Reflect.

(have the occasional drink)

Let's start with a simple warm-up.
This is called the fuck you test.

Write what is bothering you:

_____

_____

_____

_____

_____

_____

_____

_____

_____

_____

_____

_____

_____

Now, go back to this list.

Cross each worry off, one by one. But as you do, say **FUCK YOU!**

Realize these things are out of your control. There is power in embracing the expression *it is what it is.* When you accept things are what they are, your problems no longer have a hold on you because you've stopped giving a fuck about things that no longer benefit your happiness.

Every sunrise is a new opportunity to regulate your brain. Every sunset is a reminder to go to bed knowing you are important, you have a purpose, and there's a reason you exist.

If you don't know what that reason is, we'll tell you — *to be fucking happy.*

Throughout this journal, you will learn a little more about us as we guide you into each section.

Obviously, we will give you more tools and tips other than telling your problems to fuck off but it's a good first step.

FUCK OFF,
I MEAN
GOOD MORNING.

Dear Journal, it's Zak.

What a fucking day of fuckery.
Today, July 8th, 2017, my life was forever changed— not because BBC canceled Orphan Black but because I experienced something insane.
Let me back it up and mention this day started like any other. I woke up, ate three scrambled eggs, and went for my morning run around the cul-de-sac.
I was running, running, running and I stopped. It was as if my Nikes were cemented to the sidewalk. An unfamiliar feeling passed through my gut.
I didn't think too much about it. Maybe I had to take a really big shit and this was the calm before the storm. For the remainder of the run, I walked as the uneasy feeling spread through my body.
When I got back home, I did the only remedy my Iraqi mother swore by. I sat on the toilet, drank a Vernors ginger ale an attempt to shit out whatever discomfort I was experiencing.
And that's when it happened...
Instead of my ass exploding, my mind did. My entire body clenched as unwelcomed thoughts intruded. A heavy feeling of impeding doom clouded. The bathroom walls started to close in.
I screamed for my twin brother,
"Michael! I think I'm dying!"
He runs into the bathroom,
"What's wrong?"

As I sat on the toilet in a fetal position, I explained the darkness that surrounded me.

He looked at me unmediated,

"Zak, you're having an existential crisis. You're fine," he promised.

It was as if he was speaking Mandarin. What the fuck is an existential crisis and how the fuck could I be fine?

My brain kept swirling with suicidal thoughts. Odd, considering I wasn't a suicidal person.

What I experienced on July 8th, 2017 was an existential crisis. An existential crisis is a moment in which an individual questions whether their lives have meaning, purpose, or value.

I don't know why then and there, but I now know from this point on it is my duty to figure this shit out. To overcome this darkness to find my happiness.

—Until next time, Journal

MY LIFE ENDED ON THE TOILET

Journal your trigger points?

_____

_____

_____

_____

_____

_____

_____

_____

_____

_____

_____

_____

Welcome to Anxieties Anonymous! Nice to have you. We are the co-founders of this exclusive club, Michael and Zak Zakar. Here in AA, your happiness will require you to work closely with these trigger points to make the world around you less "triggering."

This book will cover all triggers from shitty family triggers to relationship triggers. With journaling, we hope to help you identify your issues and in doing so, help you understand yourself.

Finish the sentence how you see fit.

Right now, I am: _____

Finish the sentence how you see fit.

I want to be: _____

Dear Journal, it's Michael.

Why is it I only recognize happiness when I'm high?

I try not to get caught up in all the depressing bullshit in my life but it builds up. I feel I can only release when I smoke.

What is it in weed that makes it so magical?

I need to learn to merge my happiness when I'm high to the happiness when I'm sober. Like when I'm high my twin Zak is really funny, but when I'm sober he's fucking annoying.

How do I get the best of both worlds?

—Any advice, Journal?

WHAT IS HAPPINESS?

The **big** fucking question.

Google defines happiness as the state of being happy.

Wow! Big fucking help, Google.

Be your own Google and define happiness in 6 words or less.

_____

_____

_____

We like to describe happiness with these six words: *the act of doing you, unapologetically.*

Google fails to mention that happiness is defined differently for everyone. **The commonality in happiness is linked to an individual's passions.**

With passion comes happiness and with happiness comes a love for life. For example, our ultimate passion is, was, and will forever be writing. We realized the happiness writing brought us around the release of our first memoir, *Pray the Gay Away.* Our passion connected us to people struggling with similar issues of sexuality. Our passion connected us to more like-minded individuals. The more we wrote, the happier, more grounded, and connected we felt to the world.

Being a successful writer and the goals surrounding this specific passion are deciding factors on how we maneuvered around our lives.

Reaching out toward this passion of writing is how we'd figuratively die happy— *so leave a fucking Amazon review.*

To help give some guidance, let's map out your ambitions. Think of your current passion as a big goal i.e. becoming a recognized writer or getting a book deal.

What is your BIG goal?

_____

_____

With each big goal comes smaller goals as stepping stones toward achievement i.e. starting a blog or entering a writing competition.

What are the SMALLER goals
attached to it?

_____

_____

_____

_____

_____

Why do you want to achieve this goal?

_____

_____

_____

_____

_____

_____

_____

_____

_____

_____

_____

Never forget the why— it's the fuel lighting the fire under your ass.

However, if you find yourself struggling to answer any of these questions, let's spark your passions.

What was your favorite thing to do growing up?

_____

_____

_____

_____

_____

_____

What is your favorite topic to talk about?

_____

_____

_____

_____

_____

_____

Whose life do you envy and why?

_____

_____

_____

_____

_____

_____

What would you do if money wasn't
an issue?

_____

_____

_____

_____

_____

_____

Congrats!

You're beginning to unlock your true passions. From this point on start hitting those smaller goals. In doing so, you'll slowly liberate a happier you.

But you haven't passed AA just yet— now let's identify the lifestyle attached to your passions.

Dear Journal, it's Zak.

An interesting day here.

Michael and I are currently flying back from California after filming an episode of Tosh.O.

A casting producer reached out after our coming out video on YouTube went semi-viral.

The whole experience happened so fast! We got the offer Monday, flew out Wednesday, filmed our segment at 4 in the morning, and left in the same afternoon.

Michael and I popped an Adderall in to be on our best, most focused behavior... which was probably a bad idea because Michael talks too much on Adderall. Well... Michael talks too much in general.

We've never seen the show, so we didn't know what to expect.

We were interviewed from "inside a closet" while Daniel Tosh asked really random questions. And then, literally out of nowhere, the fucking Property Brothers from HGTV crash through the wall, literally.

The overall encounter was weird as fuck, but I guess that's the life of a rising star. Hopefully, the interview captured our intelligence.

Ok, Thursday at 9pm on Comedy Central. Don't forget to set your DVR, Journal.

—Xoxo, Journal

WHAT'S THE MEANING OF LIFE?

Victor Frank, an Auschwitz survivor, describes the meaning of life comes in three forms:

1. Through Work, achievement and in doing something "significant."
2. Through Love, caring for somebody else.
3. Through Courage, in face of suffering.

After our Tosh.O episode debuted, we assumed life would throw us a bone of major opportunities and life would make more sense but literally, nothing changed and life was still confusing as ever.

Through our journey to fame, we grew depressed comparing our "work" to someone like Mary-Kate and Ashleys' (before the Heath Ledger era.) We lacked fame and craved to be noticed.

Depressive thinking stems from a perspective of lacking. For instance, a mother is a prime example of someone living through love. Depression may form because this mother may feel she hasn't achieved more through her work. Keep in mind, the meaning of your life changes when presented with new challenges. "Being stuck" is a temporary feeling.

If you are someone living through courage, that courage can form into love (love for your job, love for yourself, love for change.) We had the "courage" to come out and advance that into "work." Our work as writers spreads "love."

Circle which you are living through:

Through Work

Through Love

Through Courage

The goal is not to get stuck in where you lack, but to make the most of what you have at the moment.

Live through work? Reward yourself after a promotion. Invite work-friends to something and make them your real friends. Make your interest your business.

Live through love? Start a family. Move-in with your partner. Travel, even if it's for a weekend.

Live through courage? Share your story. Move away from what no longer serves you. Work on your happiness.

Figuring out life is the meaning of life.

Let's reflect:

What does the meaning of life mean to you?

_____

_____

_____

_____

_____

_____

_____

_____

_____

_____

_____

_____

_____

_____

HAVEN'T FOUND A WAY TO SAY "FUCK YOU" POLITELY.

Dear Journal, it's Michael.

I quit my shit-ternship today!
Zak and I were working for a morning radio show in Detroit. I thought being a radio personality would be my place in this world because I love music, I'm a morning person and I love talking about myself. But I've come to find how a dream can be destroyed in 8 short weeks.

Let me add that this was a fucking internship, so we didn't get paid for this slave labor. And the 3 hosts of the radio show were fucking assholes. The hosts, whose coffee we spit in every morning had this "brilliant" idea to call our mom and come out as gay to her on-live air.

I tried explaining the seriousness of coming out to a Middle Eastern mother as this was something not to joke about.

But after saying no, the work environment quickly turned toxic. We hated the people and the industry we were in. Every morning we'd wake up to people who didn't want to see us.

So you know what we did? We fucking quit.

There are 3 kinds of dreams: your dreams, your parent's dreams, or you have no dreams.

And at the end of the day, this wasn't my dream, but a nightmare.

—Back to the drawing board, Journal

WHERE DO YOU SEE YOURSELF IN 5 YEARS?

Careers are a big trigger point. I have no fucking clue where I see myself in five years, let alone five hours.

Finding the "perfect" career is challenging because many factors play a role— *location, family ties, relationships.* When it comes to the future or talking about the future, my mind goes into overdrive.

The future you plan will **always, always, always** change. Life is not set in stone and it will **always, always, always** throw unexpected curveballs just to keep life more interesting, right? You'll need an imperfect blueprint to the supposed future but expecting spontaneous change is a part of the draft.

My sister, Bridgette, went to law school but then got pregnant. My friend, Jill, wanted an exciting life but then moved to Ohio. My dad wanted Zak and me to take over the family convenience store, but we pursued careers in entertainment— *things change.*

For most of us, the perfect job comes down to salary vs doing something we're actually passionate about with a living wage. Or maybe you have a passionate job that pays well, you lucky bitch (skip this section.)

For readers currently working toward their dream job, reflect on this thought: are you happy or content with where you are? People tend to confuse being content with being happy. **Don't confuse the two.**

What about your current job makes you happy?

_____

_____

_____

_____

_____

What is your job?

_____

_____

_____

What is your dream job?

_____

_____

_____

How far off are you from your dream job?

Think about your dream job as a big goal. What smaller goals (or small jobs) can you do to help advance you there?

A happy work-life brings a happy home-life.

And food for thought, no one knows what the fuck they're doing in their 20s, 30s, hell, even 40s.

So relax and enjoy the curveballs life WILL throw at you.

Dear Journal, it's Zak.

Welcome to Pee-Gate.

What is Pee Gate? The 2018 event that led to my firing at Monster Energy.

Yes, the gayest person in the world worked for Monster fucking Energy. Obviously, Monster wasn't my dream job but it paid the bills and I really liked my co-workers.

My boss, let's call her Karen, hated me since day one. I'm sure she was pumped for a day like this.

So basically as a Monster Brand Ambassador we drive an aggressively straight monster truck to random events around Michigan and hand out free energy drinks (we told people to "Unleash The Beast," which sounded predatory). Driving to events can take 20 minutes and sometimes take 5 hours.

On this day, Michael and I had to drove 4 hours to Illinois to pick up a shipment from the Chicago Monster unit. Midway through the shift, we couldn't stop because fucking Karen didn't want to pay overtime. I had to pee really bad... so like any other employee of the month, I peed in a water bottle.

Long story short, I forgot to take the pee bottle out of the car and Karen found the mysterious bottle to which was reported to HR.

Karen called me to tell me it was inhumane and unethical since someone could have mistaken it for a Monster (which I believe is safer to drink than a Monster.)

I tried to convince her it wasn't me but it was a very me thing to do... she even threatened to take

the pee bottle to a forensic lab for DNA testing if I
didn't fess up.

Anyway, when she fired me she sounded almost
horny.

—To unemployment we go, Journal

FUCK KAREN

Remaining positive is impossible when all you want to do is tell a co-worker to fuck off.

For instance, your supervisor, Karen, gives you a side-eye every time your fine ass enters the office.

What's Karen's problem? Did you give her a paper cut passing her yesterday's files? Did she accidentally take a sip from a random bottle of lemonade that wasn't lemonade...

What does one do when a Karen creates an unhealthy work environment?

Fuck Karen— metaphorically, not physically.

Remember our version of happiness: the act of doing you, unapologetically. This means you will have to start taking control of situations and worrying about yourself. Ultimately, **you** narrate **your** story. You are the main character of your story. Don't let side characters misguide your journey.

It's easy to say you don't care but you do, you're human. We all want to be well-liked, but not even you like everyone you meet. Some people start drama because they're bored or jealous of your potential. You're not on the same wavelength with every individual you meet.

There are thousands of different versions of you floating in the world because of a little thing called perception. Every single person you meet perceives you differently. For example, your best friend views you as their therapist with tons of tough love. Your grandma views you as a fine young individual who dresses a little slutty. Your favorite teacher views you as a miniature version of themselves. Karen views you as a dumb cunt.

In 1 word, how do you view yourself?

We can't control how others see us, but we can control how we see ourselves. Humans tend to fixate on their flaws, which reflects the worst version of themselves. Be cautious to see the version of yourself you want to be, not what you think others want you to be.

The Spotlight Effect: This effect tells us to understand and accept that people are not thinking about you as much as you think they are. Chances are most people don't care about your issues, because they have their own. At the end of the day, no one gives a fuck about what you're doing more than you do. So walk, talk and dress however you want. Many things we dislike about ourselves aren't often noticed until we, ourselves, point it out.

Remind yourself to be the version you love or the version your dog loves. In seventh grade, Zak wrote a thesis paper on why humans should be more like dogs. He got a D+ but he was on to something. If only we could see ourselves through the eyes of a dog — *unconditional love for all humans.*

The "perfect" or more lovable version of yourself starts with a healthy outlook on yourself. <u>Outlook</u> is a person's point of view or general attitude to life.

In 5 words, what is your outlook on the world?

_____

_____

_____

For our parents, mental health wasn't a thing. Well, for most foreign parents, mental health still isn't a thing.

We tend to have the same outlook as our parents because they formed what was normal for us. Whenever something in our mother's life went to shit she blamed "the Zakar Curse." A curse she swore that was passed down from our ancestors for pissing God off or something. For years, it became normalized that this idea that good things couldn't happen to average people like us because we were cursed.

**Big or Small,
What problem bothered you today?**

_____

_____

_____

Every day, you will face hefty and petty problems. Even though you feel as if these problems are some sort of higher power punishing you or that they're personal, they're not. Life is truly one problem after another and it's up to you to solve the problem or live in the mess.

A **positive** outlook makes problems to be more perceived as training wheels to a better life. Let's further your outlook with outcome. <u>Outcome</u> is the way a thing turns out. Or simply, the consequences of your actions. **Shitty choices have shitty outcomes.**

Let's assume you lost your job because you put staples in Karen's lunch. I would have gone with paperclips but you're feeling savage. When things don't go our way, we tend to want revenge or associate hate with that person or place and hold on to the anger of those shitty life curveballs.

Try embracing the unexpected change.

Fuck that place! Time to put your mental and physical energy somewhere else. If we get stuck on why something happened, we can never fully move on.

Our longtime friend lost his 10+ year position at a Detroit creative firm after a major disagreement in his workplace.

He was devastated. He was let go in his 50's with no solid plan of what to do or where to go next because his daily routine was disrupted.

You (the narrator) determine how this story ends (the outcome).

What did he do? He didn't stand in place hoping something would magically happen. He simply took action into his own hands. He moved from Michigan to Fort Lauderdale merely because he hated Michigan winters. He knew his passion and found a job he loved in the same field with more pay, just by moving away from what no longer served him. He met his now-boyfriend and has never been happier. He claims being fired was the best thing that happened to him. Our reactions are defining moments to who we are.

What past challenge turned out to serve you?

_____

_____

_____

_____

_____

_____

_____

_____

_____

_____

How do you usually handle stress? Are these methods working? What could you do instead to better manage your stress?

_____

_____

_____

_____

_____

_____

_____

_____

_____

We're not encouraging you to get fired from your job and move to Florida, you've seen how they've handled the covid pandemic. We're saying what looks like the end might be a new beginning, but you'll never find peace if you panic in the present.

Positive thinking can be good for your
physical health, why do you think that is?

_____

_____

_____

_____

_____

_____

_____

_____

_____

_____

_____

Dear Journal, it's Michael.

I have some exciting fucking news!
Unlike Zak, I'm not an idiot and pissed in a water bottle, but I quit my job at Monster Energy today.
That's not the good news.
A production company wants to turn our independent memoir, Pray the Gay Away, into a national stage play!
I'm a little nervous because the company wants us to play ourselves. Sounds easy but we don't have much stage experience besides Tosh.O and the one open-mic night where we got booed off-stage.
I don't know what I expected when we wrote Pray the Gay Away but I didn't expect it to get optioned as a play. What a random curveball from life! Things finally seem like they're working in my favor.
Wish me luck. I have to go start prepping for the perfect orgasm on-stage. I've faked a few so I'm confident I can do this.

—Break a leg, Journal

VIOLA DAVIS CONFIDENCE

Can you recall a time where you made plans and nothing went accordingly? **That is part of life.** Nothing in life goes according to plan and being able to accept that is key.

With high **expectations**, we expect more than what is realistically given in a situation. Lowering your expectations will allow you to take things as they come.

How many times have you been let down because you expected too much out of a person or situation?

And what happens when we are let down? We spiral.

For us, our confidence dissipated as we endured mental abuse backstage. Confidence was lost as two directors quit mid-show. Our confidence was destroyed as I expected this play to catapult my happiness when in reality none of my exceptions were met.

When I thought about confidence, I thought I would only have to apply it to my acting but confidence attributes to how we walk and talk. We believe someone who is fully confident is fully capable of being happy. Have you ever seen a sad confident person?

On a scale of 1 to 10, circle your confidence:

0   1   2   3   4   5   6   7   8   9   10

Confidence is a full-body effect. It's being confident when you're with people, alone, during the day, at

---

CONFIDENCE CONSISTS OF:

eye contact.

learning to say no.
(without feeling bad about it)

not feeling the need to be validated from people you wouldn't take advice from.

practicing alone-time.

not talking negatively about people.
(including yourself)

good posture.

stop saying sorry.
(unless you hurt someone's feelings, eliminate the word from your vocabulary)

---

night, etc.

If one doesn't have confidence, fake it. It's like acting. When you fake it for so long, it slowly becomes real or second nature. This takes the power to pull your best attributes forward and push your insecurities to the back. The show must go on and they're waiting for you. Whether you get applause or boos is up to you.

For me, confidence had to be rebuilt after I walked

away from something I expected too much from.

Sometimes you have to channel Viola Davis-sized confidence just to enter the world. I mean, have you seen that bitch act? Jesus H Christ!

Name someone you find confident:

_____

What about this person makes you perceive them as confident?

_____

_____

_____

_____

Now let's talk about confidence's enemy: rejection. Confidence gets muffled by rejection because rejection is pain. Take rejection as feedback to strengthen your confidence. This is why children appear so confident, their souls are pure with no concept of rejection yet. Good things take time, so expect to run into plenty of rejection. Our outlook tells us rejection is protection. Your rejections don't define you, how you learn from them does.

What person's rejection hurts you most?

_____

This doesn't mean you're not good enough; it means this person has failed to notice what you have to offer.

So come on, what have we learned? Yes, say it with us, "fuck them!"

Now say it confidently like Viola Davis.

Write a pep talk to yourself:

_____

_____

_____

_____

_____

_____

_____

_____

WELL,
FUUUUUUCK.

Dear Journal, it's Zak.

It happened. I killed my grandma...
I'm kidding! But no really, my grandma died last week.

And not to sound like a little bitch but now we have to go to a funeral. I fucking hate funerals.

Middle Eastern funerals are the worst, they're nothing like American funerals. American funerals last like 5 minutes and everyone moves on with their lives. At Middle Eastern funerals we're required to mourn for 6 fucking months. Being forced to be sad for 6 months is so... sad.

Also, at Middle Eastern funerals we hire this old lady who walks into funerals not knowing a single person and yells sad shit at the guests hoping to induce them into a deeper state of depression.

At my grandma's funeral, she screamed at my mom, "your mom's never coming back."

Regardless of all this, I noticed I didn't cry at the funeral. My grandma and I weren't best friends but I still loved her.

Am I emotionally fucked-up?

—Say no, Journal

YOU ARE AN EMOTIONAL MACHINE

As humans, being happy *all the time* **isn't realistic.** Different emotions carry different leverage on the body and mind. Sadness is the heaviest as it sticks to your conscience. Whereas, happiness is weightless as it bounces off or fades away.

Emotions are complex. Being depressed is more than being sad. Being anxious is more than being worried. When we understand our emotions, we understand ourselves and when we understand ourselves, we start to understand life.

All emotions need to be felt, accepted, processed and understood. Of all your emotions, let's discuss the one that ruins the present and clouds the future: **worry.**

Worrying is a dangerous emotion we inherited the moment we left the womb— *Thanks, Mom!*

Worry devoured our brains as our minds were in a consent hold to worst-case scenarios. We'd be mid-flight thinking: *"Hmm what a great day for this plane to go down."* Our intense focus on the negative outweighed the positive. We worried about the next existential crisis because at some point we had to crash again, right? Wrong.

Like the plane, we should've been excited to land, not waiting to crash.

When we worry, we lose pieces of ourselves. We lose confidence in the world around us. Once it gains access to one's mind, worrying gains dangerous superpowers: loss of time, guilt-induced thoughts, disturbed sleep, short-term memory.

Overcoming worry takes the art of truly not giving a fuck. Worry fades when we let go of things outside of our control— *it is what it is.*

Nine times out of ten, let the world play itself out. No amount of guilt will change your past and no amount of anxiety will change the future. The future has not happened yet so don't worry.

We all process our emotions differently.

Word Association,
write the first thing that comes to mind:

anger: _____   fear: _____

sadness: _____   disgust: _____

joy: _____   trust: _____

annoying: _____   candy corn: _____

Dear Journal, it's Michael.

Okay, I'm bored in the house and I'm in the house bored. Bored in the house and I'm in the house bored. Bored than a motherfucker, in the house bored. And I'm bored than a motherfucker, in the house bored. Bored in the house, bored in the house bored. Bored in the house, bored in the house bored. I'm bored than a motherfucker, in the house bored. And I'm bored than a motherfucker, in the house bored.

> —Journal, I am so fucking bored
> that I put a 10-piece McNugget
> on a Hot-N-Ready

ARE YOU SAD OR BORED?

Truly a valid question.

As humans, we call for constant stimulation. The moment we aren't, we're sad.

We didn't realize boredom was a dangerous emotion until boredom devoured our fucking lives— *no surprises, no spice, the same mundane schedule driving us slowly insane.*

Humans naturally self-sabotage themselves and a big part of that is contributed to boredom. With boredom comes free time and with free time comes more time to think about your insecurities, mistakes, and past decisions. People who are either sad or bored hold on to these useless thoughts.

Overcoming boredom is simple, keep your mind stimulated— *it's the motivation that's hard.*

MOTIVATION CONSISTS OF:

taking small steps in new goals.
(progress not perfection)

taking negative people out of the equation.

making a daily to-do list before bed.
(structure)

if something takes less than 2 minutes, do it.

leaving the past in the past.

comparing your journey to your journey only.

Dear Journal, it's Zak,

I hate being the smart twin.
I'm already the more attractive twin, what's left for poor little Michael?
Today, we were interviewed by Fox News about our book. I mentioned our up-and-coming play, our coming out, and Middle Eastern culture.
And Michael... well Michael talked about blowjobs during the 8:45 morning segment.
I don't know why but in high-pressure situations Michael gets so awkward, loses focus, and word-vomits... fucking idiot.

—Should I kill Michael and go solo, Journal?

EYES ON THE OSCAR

Losing focus is something "sad" people have in common. We become so blinded by the bad and the future of the bad, nothing but the bad that it becomes all we can focus on.

How can one be happy when one expects future disappointment?

Focus on the importance of **now**.

Delete the idea of a future from your head. The supposed future doesn't exist. There is only **now**. Your worry draws you to project problems that exist in the future and the future doesn't exist, so if you keep your focus on the now those future sadnesses will essentially never come.

My existential crisis was a result of losing complete control of my focus. Your time is your focused energy — *stop waiting and start doing.*

One of our big goals is to win an Oscar. You read it first, we're putting it in writing and manifesting it! And no, Michael will not be giving the speech.

Write an acceptance speech to yourself.
What do you promise for yourself?
Who are you thankful for? What are you
thankful for?

_____

_____

_____

_____

_____

_____

_____

_____

_____

_____

_____

Bravo! *standing ovation*

Dear Journal, it's Michael.

I regret my new tattoo.

But, if you don't regret at least 1 tattoo, did you even get a tattoo?

The tattoo is a portrait of my mom smiling proudly on my right thigh— I got it as retaliation for her not accepting my coming out. So now, every time a guy tries to blow me, he has to see my mom judging them.

I should have thought about this tattoo a little more... at least it's better than my "smooth sailing" tattoo on my forearm. It's in Arabic but wrongly translates to "P folder sailing."

—I'm still gonna rock it, Journal

THE HUMAN EXPERIMENT

List 3 things you regret:

1._____

_____

2._____

_____

3._____

_____

Now tell us why you regret each one:

1._____

_____

2._____

_____

3._____

_____

We call this the human experiment to remind you that **you're a fucking human.** You're not perfect and this means you'll make big mistakes like sleeping with your friend's dad or keying your ex's car (both Michael has done).

Regret sits heavy.

Look at what you wrote. Learn from your mistakes. These wrongs happened in the past and we're in the **now.**

Be better and do better now. You have new challenges ahead. Don't let yesterday's mistakes ruin tomorrow's progress. Show us with action, not thoughts.

What can you do different tomorrow?

_____

_____

_____

_____

_____

_____

_____

EVIL FUCKING TWINS (NOT US)

Dear Journal, it's Michael.

I had my first existential crisis— on my 22nd birthday of all fucking days.

I was celebrating at a local gay bar during their foam night. I was on the back patio surrounded by bubbles like a toddler in a bath when suddenly this feeling crept out of nowhere.

I tried not to panic as I froze.

I couldn't recognize my friend's smiles as they danced in the foam. I was watching them in slow motion. It felt like an out-of-body experience (I think they call this disassociation?)

Everything appeared pointless at that moment. Everyone around me felt dead and I couldn't un-think it. My brain filled with dread to the point where I couldn't breathe.

I haven't eaten in 3 days or told anyone cause I'm not really sure how to process these feelings without sounding crazy.

—I don't know about you
but I'm feeling 22, Journal

EVIL TWIN 1

Being sad makes more sense. *Why?*
Think about it. The world is wired so fucking
negatively— *the education system, housing, healthcare,
anything for women.* As a result, this makes our brains
wired negatively. Our mindsets view happiness as an
illusion more than a reality.
So now you're asking,
*"Michael and Zak, how do we make this fantasy a
reality?"*
We'll tell you but it's tricky to explain with a couple
of words hence why we wrote an entire book on it.

Up to this point, we've discussed basic emotions,
your outlook on life, career advice, but now we're
going to discuss the evil twins driving any event from
bad to worse: *overthinking* and *second-guessing.*

These two appear to be twins because they seem
alike (evil) but they are very very different.

The first twin: overthinking. Overthinking is the
inability to get outside of one's head. Overthinking is
the one, if not the most important obstacle to
overcome on your path of happiness.

Post-existential crisis, overthinking became my new
frienemy. Once an extrovert, now an introvert as my
confidence slowly disappeared. I spent hours
overthinking situations of outcomes that would never
happen. Overthinking creates this snowball effect
leading to one emotion we are all familiar with:
depression.

Are you an over-thinker?
Check all that apply.

☐ You are in a constant state of worry.

☐ Your inability to enjoy the present moment.

☐ You often replay memories in your head and think "what if I did this differently."

☐ You have trouble sleeping because you can't shut your fucking brain off.

☐ You are indecisive.

☐ You exist.

Yeah, overthinking fucking sucks.

To become in control of yourself, you must control your ability to overthink and it takes a lot of overthinking to stop overthinking. Remember thinking isn't doing. Doing is doing. Overthinking is wasted, unfocused energy.

Usually, when we are faced with a problem, the problem is rarely the problem. A majority of the problem is caused by the "what if's" in our heads.

How is it this hard not to think? We did it four years straight in high school.

Overthinking flows in pockets when we feel lost, confused, or lesser than. It's like when you play that stupid mental game, where you tell yourself everything will be fine IF this hypothetical situation doesn't happen. I'll be alright *if* I make *that* green light I'm driving toward. Then the light turns yellow, your heart skips a beat, you tell yourself "it didn't count" and add this weird unnecessary stress onto your day. Habits like this are your insecurities feeding away at your brain because it's looking for guidance or some sign that everything will be okay.

Here's that fucking sign: **everything will be okay.**

With overthinking, remember not to get hung up on how things are supposed to be. Develop a more go-with-the-flow attitude. You are a river, not a rock. Teach yourself not to ponder every single option that may or may not play out and realize there is *one* choice and that is *your* choice because your choice is the *right* choice.

What do you over-think about?
Why is this your immediate focus?

_____

_____

_____

_____

_____

_____

_____

This list should look similar to the first exercise of things that bother you. Like what's bothering you, the things you overthink about are outside your control— *you know what to do. Tell the things that make you overthink to fuck off. You have better things to think about!*

Whenever you feel yourself becoming stuck in your head, try the 5-4-3-2-1 technique to stay grounded.

What are 5 things you can see? Look for small details, objects you've never noticed

What are 4 things you can feel? Notice the sensation against your fingertips.

What are 3 things you can hear? Pay attention to sounds that your mind has tuned out.

What are 2 things you can smell? Describe the smell.

What is 1 thing you can taste? Start carrying mints or gum.

Focus, stay present and stop letting your mind be in a constant struggle of what's "right." You can stabilize this by simply making a fucking choice.

Dear Journal, it's Zak.

My boyfriend of 3 years moved to fucking Philadelphia today.

We're going to try and make it work but I don't know if I'm ready for a long-distance relationship.

Why couldn't he move somewhere closer? I'm a fucking Pisces, do you know how much attention we need?

We'll see...maybe it's time to be a hoe again... or maybe I'll murder him...

I'm gonna get a McFlurry and contemplate all this shit.

—I need a fucking drink, Journal

EVIL TWIN 2

The second twin: second-guessing.

A happier person is a person whose able to make a fucking choice. Indecisive people have this inner fear that whatever choice is being made is wrong. Having this type of outlook blocks happiness.

Most choices (or outcomes) are black and white. The problem? We spend more time lingering in the grey area.

Around 25, I entered a long-distance relationship because I believed in love like a Disney princess. I second-guessed my choices because my overthinking mentality created this "grass is greener" effect. This tiring effect made my relationship miserable because I second-guessed my second-guesses. My choices were polluted with doubt. If I traveled to my then-boyfriend, I had major FOMO from whatever my friends were doing. If I hung out with friends in Michigan, I wished I was with my ex miles away. As time passed, I began to spread myself too thin, not knowing where I wanted to be or what I wanted to do. Being a people pleaser, I tried to make everyone happy except the only person that fucking mattered: **me.**

As a result, I got dumped and lost a couple of friends. I didn't know which side of the grass was more green because I was stuck on the fence.

In your journey of happiness, you must be able to make a choice and stick to it with no regrets. You are training your brain to shut off the anxieties of options B, C, and D when you commit happily to A.

As humans, we are under the impression that making choices to serve ourselves is selfish or greedy when we fail to realize if it doesn't benefit you, physically or emotionally, then it serves you no purpose. If it doesn't bring you an orgasm, inspiration, or income, give it no attention.

Circle One:

Chipotle   or   Qdoba?

Congrats— *you made a fucking choice! (Chipotle, obviously).*

Let's nosedive into a big life lesson that took us years to master: **enjoying the moment.**

Enjoying the moment takes the power of being present. When you commit to one path you must be present in it. Happiness is unachievable if you are constantly living in your head. Being present in the now takes training and is challenging for over-thinkers.

The short version: realizing that the best part of any trip is not the destination but the drive there.

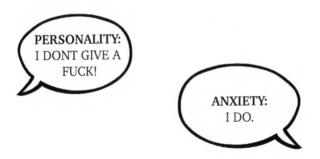

67

if you're ever unsure of a choice,
come back to this page and let the universe
decide for you
*(close your eyes, ask a yes or no question, and
randomly point to any part of this page).*

No. No. No. Yes. Yes. No. Ask Later. 100%.
Doesn't Look Good. Fuck No. Yes. Totally.
We think not. Yes. Yes. Yes. No. Absolutely.
Ask a Friend. Do It. Are you fucking crazy?
No. Absolutely Not. For sure. Yes, bitch. No!
Doesn't Look Good. Yes. You're Crazy.
Give It A Go. Does It Make You Happy?
Seems okay! Don't Do It. Heck no. Yasss!
Totes. You bet. Not this time. Undoubtedly.
No fucking way. Probably not, bud.
Nods in approval You should pass. Yes. No.
No. Yes. No. Yes. Yes. No. Ask Later.
Doesn't Look Good. Fuck No. Yes. Totally.
We think not. Yes. Yes.Yes. No. Absolutely.
Ask a Friend. Do It. Are you fucking crazy?
No. Absolutely Not. For sure. Yes, bitch. No!
Yes. The world isn't in favor of it.
Are you doing this because you're bored?
Don't Do It. Heck no. Yasss! Totes. You bet.

C'EST LA
FUCKING VIE

Dear Journal, it's Michael.

For the last month, Zak and I have been traveling with the drag queens from RuPaul's Drag Race on a 40-city tour promoting our play during their show's intermission.

Tour bus life is fucking weird— you live out of your suitcase and wake up in a new city every day with dozens of strangers trying not to invade what little personal space you have.

I was hoping it would feel like one big family but in reality, everyone on the bus treats Zak and me as the red-headed step-children.

Zak and I are putting way too much energy to make friends, but we became the butt of every joke. Every time, we walk into a room, everyone goes purposely quiet until we leave. We even went out of our way to get everyone a Christmas present but all we got was coal.

Why am I trying to get approval from people that I want to throw in front of a moving train?

—Next stop Seattle, Journal

P.S. Fuck you, Mary-Beth.

THE IPHONE WITH A HORRIBLE DATA PLAN

Think of energy literally. Energy is the battery life and you are the iPhone.

Perhaps you're an iPhone 5C, a bit slower to process things than someone who is an iPhone 12. Maybe you're an Android and no one sees the potential in you. Regardless, we're going to ask you to process this thought: for one full day, your energy is at 100% battery life. How are you going to use this battery?

How much energy are you spending on one person, one place, or one thing? Are you spending the day scrolling on Facebook when other apps need your attention? Everyone starts the day with a full battery. Learn to use your battery life on apps that matter or you'll constantly be charging yourself. Do you notice how much faster your phone works when you delete apps, old pictures and upgrade the software?

As an iPhone, what song would be your ringtone?

_____

_____

This is your new anthem, baby. Before moving on, listen to this song.

WATER BREAK!

You are a sunflower.
Sunflowers rise toward the sun. Look for
the light, water your roots, and bloom. So
drink a glass of water, you dehydrated bitch.
Your body is 60% water. Drink up
because we need your brain to keep
processing what it's reading.

Bottoms up.

Journal anything:

Dear Journal, it's Zak.

My mom said Covid is happening because God is mad at people.

—Journal, what the fuck did we do?

YOUR INNER BUDDHA

A major factor that plays in an individual's outlook is **religion**. Religion plays a large component in how we view, respond, and interact with others. For some, religion tells us how to be happy.

For us, growing up gay caused mental conflict with the teachings of Christianity. We were born into a religion with no choice. To believe what our parents believed without question. According to our beliefs, we were born wrong. Our minds were wrong. Our brains wired negatively because we felt like the person who created us wanted us to burn in Hell for being our authentic selves.

Every religion has a similar framework, just reworded, reprised, and reworked. However, in our college studies, we did learn about a religion that made more sense to us at a time we felt lost: Buddhism.

Buddhism puts focus and faith into oneself instead of some bigger unknown being.

We drifted away from Christianity because we grew tired of being told to pray for things to get better. Pray in the hopes this shitty world would work in our favor. To pray the gay away. Not to worry because God's got your back every step of the way *if* you follow His every word.

In contrast, Buddhist teachings encourage one to work happily for their goals.

Let's tap into your inner Buddha.

"Self-love is the greatest medicine."
-Buddha

Like we mentioned earlier, life is one big problem after another. Buddhism teachings solve a problem in 1 of 3 ways:

1. Accept it.
2. Change it.
3. Leave it.

"If you can't accept it, change it. If you can't change it, leave it."

Your happiness will need you to become a more realistic person. Someone who accepts the realities of a situation. *Accept it, change it or leave it.*

As we get deeper into the basic laws of Buddhism, teachings encourage a life with no attachments. We don't fully accept that, so we're going to change it.

Lesser attachments— *your journey of happiness will need you to detach from what doesn't benefit or value you.*

Name someone or something in your life you'd like to give less attention to:

_____

_____

Why?

_____

_____

_____

_____

Let go.

The overall goal of Buddhism? Finding inner peace within yourself. With peace brings happiness.

FINDING INNER PEACE CONSISTS OF:

focusing on things in your control/
letting go of what you cannot.

being present in the now.

accepting the now.

being honest with yourself.

don't beg.
(what is yours, will come— law of attraction,
bitch)

forgiving yourself.

finding a mirror and repeating after us: *I'm that bitch. Been that bitch, still that bitch, will forever be that bitch.*

Dear Journal, it's Michael.

Sorry to be short, I'm in a hurry... I'm about to be arrested.
I would write more but I know the police are on their way and I need to look cute for my mug shot.

—Will you be my one phone call, Journal?

CAN'T LOCK UP HAPPINESS

When trying to be a happier person all I received from the universe was anger. For coming out, I found it difficult to be happy when so much anger was built up from hiding my true self with no real career path. This anger only intensified when the person I wanted to turn to most threw holy water at me after coming out.

My anger and resentment formed a chain reaction of shoplifting. For me, stealing was the only thing I found joy in.

On my mother's 52nd birthday, I was arrested for stealing her birthday present at Kmart. My arrest was a result of me losing focus of my happiness and a direct focus on my anger.

 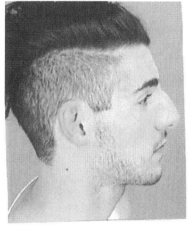

Michael's mugshot, which hangs proudly above Zak's bed.

Let's discuss this dangerous emotion because anger blocks inner peace, logical thought, and a healthy relationship with your emotions.

When do you notice your anger most?

_____

_____

_____

_____

_____

_____

_____

_____

Take a breather when needed and ask yourself what your anger is trying to tell you about yourself.

Anger is fear in disguise. Fear (and the anger that stems from it) is a collection of past traumas you are holding on to. Fear is trying to control situations you don't have control over. Are you scared? Good. **No growth is done with comfortability.**

It's time to release.

Write what you want to get off your chest:

_____

_____

_____

_____

_____

_____

_____

_____

Hold on to these for too long and you'll fall into a slump of depression. This doesn't mean you will be stuck in this version of yourself. It's knowing not to continue that cycle so it doesn't become your norm.

When you feel angry **stop, breathe, and assess.**

Remember surviving the day is an accomplishment in itself. Society puts too much emphasis on being good. Sometimes when we're sad or angry, we don't want to hear have a good day. It's okay to have a day. A day where it's okay to be alive. Things will get better but for now, have a day.

One way to break from the cycle of wrath is learning to be more accountable for your actions.

One time you should have said sorry but didn't:

_____

_____

_____

_____

_____

_____

Don't feel bad. You were hurt and weren't ready to say sorry yet.

One bad habit you want to try to quit:

_____

_____

_____

You fucked up today and that's okay. Humans fuck up. No matter how old we get, we are never too old to learn and grow from our mistakes.

Another lesson from Buddhism: meditation.

Praying for me turned into meditation. I can feel a higher version of myself begging to reach my full potential.

MEDITATION TIPS:

create a safe quiet space.

meditation is manifestation.

let thoughts come and go.

breathe through your nose.

mediation isn't a one time
thing, keep practicing.

turn off your phone.

This taught me to identify my central issues. One being anger. The second being self-love.

Self-love is more important than real love. If you can't love yourself, how can you expect others to love you? I know, a shitty way of quoting RuPaul.

Dear Journal, it's Zak.

   Sorry for the late-night entry, couldn't sleep and my brain hurts.
   So my boyfriend moved back from Philly to Michigan! We somehow survived with all the distance. We've gotten even closer these past couple of months but yesterday he got a job offer in Chicago.
   Traveling from Michigan to Chicago seems more doable but God can you give me a fucking break?

                              —Night, Journal

SLEEPING BEAUTY

With anger comes a bitchy sleep-deprived version of yourself.

Sleep— *a luxury for adults.*

Aren't you jealous of people who close their eyes and somehow magically fall asleep? *What kind of witchcraft is that?*

We've tried weighted blankets, but they suffocated us. We drank warm milk and tea before bed, but it made us get up and use the bathroom all night. The only thing that made us more sleepy was scrolling through our phones until our eyes bled dry.

Being well-rested will let you access more of your emotional range. A well-rested bitch is a bitch ready to take on the world.

History Lesson:
The sleep industry is a $70 billion industry. Humans are supposed to be segment sleepers— meaning we sleep in segments during the day. But thanks to Henry Ford, we sleep 8 hours to prepare us for our 9-to-5 work life.

First, create a sleep space that makes sense for you. Like a mediation space, you need to create an environment your body's comfortable with. *Do you need a fan while you sleep? TV playing in the background?*

You sleep a third of your life so invest in your comfort.

Your sleep is directly correlated with your stress. Managing your stress is the biggest obstacle to overcome when trying to obtain a better sleep schedule.

What is the last thing you think about that blocks your sleep?

_____

_____

_____

_____

For a healthier sleep, what you wrote is your biggest problem to overcome. Resolve this thought and your sleep will come easier. Sleep with an easy heart. This means going to bed and forgiving everyone, including yourself.

The sun will rise and the sun will set. You have more chances to try again. Happiness is when going to sleep is no longer a means of escape.

WE'LL BE
FRIENDS FOREVER
BECAUSE
YOU KNOW
TOO FUCKING
MUCH

Dear Journal, it's Michael.

An actual conversation I had with my mom today:

-Hey Michael, did you open the
 can of peanuts?
-No.
-Did I open it?
-I don't know, Mom.
-Do you think Zak opened it?
-I don't know, Mom.
-What if someone spit in it and
 left it on the shelf?
-No Mom, no one spit in your peanuts.
-How do you know that?...so you're
 sure you didn't open the peanuts?
-Mom, eat the fucking peanuts!
-I should throw them away just in case.

This happens over and over as Mom doubts the safety of every grocery she didn't personally open herself.
...she's driving me crazy.

—Time to order DoorDash, Journal

MOVE OUT OF YOUR PARENT'S FUCKING HOUSE

Parents— *the source of our pain and suffering.*
There are two types of parents:
> *-parents who shower their children with unconditional love and support.*
> *-parents that remind you of your constant failures (usually foreign parents).*

Regardless, either parent is a blessing— *with a healthy outlook, of course!*

Your parents are guidelines, not guides on how to live your life. We tend to forget that our parents are human too. They will make mistakes. They will make poor choices that affect you.

Don't let your parent's trauma become your trauma. When it comes to parental figures, take away their best traits. Our mother claims we didn't have a normal childhood because we were poor and not white but we thank our mother for being a nervous wreck. It made us wary when it came to business. We thank our Dad for his easy-going attitude. It made us follow our passions.

List 2 traits you like from each parent:

Mom (or parental figure):

1._____

_____

2._____

_____

Dad (or parental figure):

1._____

_____

2._____

_____

One thing you would get rid of from both:

1._____

_____

2._____

_____

For readers with shitty relationships with their parents, sometimes family means nothing if all they add to your life is toxicity— it's okay to cut ties with blood to savage your happiness. **If you didn't come from a healthy family, make sure a healthy family comes from you.**

Dear Journal, It's Michael.

Today is Zak and I's 27th birthday.

It has been a decade since we've been out. A decade of battling Mom on our sexuality. The same woman who threw away last year's birthday cake because it had pink frosting did something unexpected at dinner.

She surprised us with a pint of rainbow ice cream.

"You know, 'cause you're like that" is what she said.

It definitely wasn't the hug we needed, but it was a small thing that made a huge difference. She's making an effort in her own way.

#FeelingLoved.

—Have a good night, Journal

THE SMALL THINGS

Write a time in your life you consider to be a "small things" moment that made a big impact:

_____

_____

_____

_____

_____

_____

_____

_____

_____

_____

Reflect on this moment of your life. It's cliche but enjoy the small things— unless it's your ex-boyfriend's penis.

Dear Journal, it's Zak.

Finding friends post-high school is very challenging. How the fuck does one just go up to someone they think is not stupid and become forever friends?

We should base strangers on their Halloween costumes.

Go with me on this, Journal.

You can perceive a lot by somebody's costume. If someone has a handmade costume, this means that type of person craves attention and is a people pleaser (my kind of people.) If they buy a generic costume from the store means they are simple people who enjoy the fun, but not the spotlight. If they don't dress up, this means they are the type of person who doesn't appreciate the small things in life.

Does that make sense? Probably not.

Whatever it's my journal, I can write whatever the fuck I want.

I need more friends... my twin brother isn't cutting it anymore.

— TTYL, Journal

FRIENDS WITH BENEFITS

Think of all potential friends as auras. An <u>aura</u> is a reflection of who you are.

We view auras as colors. Think of these colors being reflected off your emotions. Whatever color you are that day, contrasts or compliments with other colors. And your best color comes from being your most authentic self. People are attracted to happy people and a happier person is a more authentic person. We defined happiness as the "act of doing you, unapologetically" and we'd define being authentic as the same. Connecting to your authentic self will magnetize the right people around you.

As you start to outgrow old friends and make new ones, you'll find yourself experimenting with new people, new drugs, new activities you thought you would never try just in the hopes of making a new friend.

As you go through this experimental phase of friends, remember to stay authentic (otherwise you will find fake friends or become the fake friend.)

> **BEING AUTHENTIC CONSISTS OF:**
>
> acceptance.
> (accepting yourself, accepting your flaws, another
> way of saying *it is what it is*)
>
> not people-pleasing.
>
> learning to listen to your gut instead of your brain.
> (the brain will start to overthink and stop you from
> making authentic calls)
>
> being present and actively listening.
>
> expressing yourself.
> (when it matters to you)
>
> not gossiping.
> (or limiting it, you sassy bitch)

Ok great, you're more authentic now... so how the fuck do you make friends?

To make friends as an adult takes two easy steps: one, to make a friend, you have to be a friend, and two, show up somewhere regularly. The reason we make friends in high school and or work is because we see these people regularly. So find a class or place that interests you— rock climbing, a nice café, a painting class, kickboxing, etc. and you're bound to make friends when you become a familiar face where people share your interests.

Let's identify what you're looking for in a friend:

What qualities do you look for in a person, non-romantic?

Write about a quality your best friend has that you admire:

What are the responsibilities of friendship?

Would you rather have many casual
friends or a few close friends?

_____

Who have you been friends with the longest?
Write about it:

_____

_____

_____

What makes a friend a "best friend"?

_____

_____

_____

_____

What is your favorite way to talk to friends—
phone, in person, or text?

_____

Have you ever made friends with someone
you didn't initially like? how did it happen?

_____

_____

_____

_____

_____

_____

_____

_____

_____

_____

_____

_____

_____

ANOTHER WATER BREAK!

Done?
Ok. Continue.

WE'D LOVE TO GET FUCKED BY SOMEONE OTHER THAN LIFE.

Dear Journal, it's Zak.

Soooooo I feel like dying.

I know super fucking dramatic but I got dumped... I think? I don't know. I'm so fucking confused and feel like I'm losing my mind.

After years of fighting for this stupid fucking relationship from state to state, he wants a break. We are not fucking Ross and Rachel from Friends— NO BREAKS.

Life fucking sucks... love fucking sucks... everything fucking sucks!

Depressed and confused. Is this adulthood?

—Fuck off, Journal

THE EX I WANTED TO MURDER

Break-ups are traumatizing. Short of death, I don't know anything more traumatizing than love.

Dating, love, *those* mushy-gushy feelings need their own chapter. Fuck, they need their own book.

Our first piece of dating advice— *don't*.

Kidding. Love is a beautiful thing.

With the ex I wanted to murder, I felt as if I met my soulmate. He surpassed every guy before him. We managed to stay together after his move to Philadelphia. We managed to stay together while I traveled for a year. We managed to survive the impossible!

The relationship was pure love for about two years. In year three, things took a turn for the worst after he got a job offer in Chicago and one thing became damaged— *our communication*.

We decided to take a break (well, he decided) as he needed an unknown amount of time to "find himself" and that meant without me. I struggled to understand what exactly that meant as I was willing to do the distance and work around his needs.

He said not to worry because we'd come back together in the future. Two weeks turned into eight months.

Once your brain decides it likes someone, the brain will create excuses for red flags.

He unintentionally held me at an arm's length while trying to figure his shit out. I struggled big-time not knowing if I should move on with my life or wait for the love of my life to come back to me.

Three more months passed. My patience was tested as we talked less and argued more.

This toxicity taught me an important red flag in humans: inconsistency. I lost love for a person who was becoming inconsistent with my emotions. I lost love for myself. I was filled with hate and lost the right of narrating my own story because I became a wandering side character in someone else's story. Heartbreak wasn't sudden, but slow and painful. He worked on the now, while I was stuck in the past.

Humans find themselves accepting physical and mental damage from significant others because our brains tell us we're in love. We stay in toxic situations because we fail to understand what is happening while it's happening. We endure months, even years of damage because of this love illusion. This illusion assured me that I would never find love again so endure the trauma or suffer dying alone.

"Pain is certain, suffering is optional."
-Buddha

With love, we need to understand that sometimes people come into our lives that make us feel happy. We want so badly to hold on to that happy feeling for as long as we can. We focus too much on trying to prolong and protect that fucking feeling instead of enjoying those small moments. We drag out these moments to give us that illusion of future happiness. But it was just that— *a moment.*

Realize and accept that. The moment has passed. Love is easy to find, but also it's easy to lose— *it's a teeter-totter. You will find those happy moments again.*

Everyone is on their own journey to happiness. I

kept victimizing myself when I realized my "soulmate" moved on because I no longer aligned to his journey of happiness. It took months for me to accept that everyone is on their own journey of happiness.

WHEN DEALING WITH LOVE:

don't let mixed signals fool you.

past affection isn't current affection.

indecision is a decision.

don't be a go-to person to someone you can't go to.

only seeing the best in someone who continually hurts you is denial.

don't confuse physical love for mental love.

"they are the right person at
the wrong time!"
(in reality this means they're the wrong person
because the right people
are timeless)

they're not your soulmate because your soulmate would actually add to your happiness— *that simple.*

...And this goes without saying but don't murder your ex. It's not worth it. You have to figure out where to hide the body, burn your clothes, write a fake suicide note. Just move on it's easier.

What did your first major
break up teach you?

_____

_____

_____

_____

_____

_____

_____

_____

_____

_____

Dear Journal, it's Michael.

I'm gonna stop chasing my first boyfriend.

It's been five years and I can't stop looking at his life on Facebook. His life isn't even that exciting! I just miss his stupid face.

It's not healthy for me to like all his posts and keep tabs on his Aunt Sharon. I have to stop hoping he'll come back for me when I'm the one that cheated.

But is sending a dick pic on Snapchat really cheating, Journal?

Oh my God! He just posted a picture of him and his new boyfriend.

Please hold, I need to stalk.

...

Obviously, he's not as cute as me but they look happy... happier than we were.

Who am I to ruin someone's happiness? Maybe it's for the best. I mean, he is a real estate agent with a degree in botany.

                    —Best Thing I Never Had, Journal

MOVING ON IS UNINTENTIONAL REVENGE

Break-up or make-up?

As we try to make the "perfect" life, most long-term relationships undergo some sort of break. "Perfect" relationships come with their own set of unique rules and problems.

Love shouldn't be complex. If it works, it works. On the other hand, it's complex because genuine love takes sacrifice.

Make-up. A relationship is only worth saving if both parties have the will to fight.

Break-up. When the fight for love becomes one-sided.

Chasing someone? Let's decide this relationship is a relationship or a relationshit.
For each question, circle A or B.

1) A. Do you miss the person?

    B. Do you miss the routine?

2) A. They are fighting to show me they still want us.

    B. They give me crumbs I confuse for cake.

3) A. Communication is clear.

   B. You keep invalidating your emotions to validate theirs.

4) A. Trust is still there.

   B. Trust is lost.

5) A. They make me happy.

   B. They made me happy.

6) A. You don't pry on their social media.

   B. You stalk their social media an unhealthy amount.

7) A. They make you feel safe.

   B. You find myself second-guessing every action and text.

If you circled more A's: *make-up.* If you circled more B's: *break-up.*

Dear Journal, it's Michael.

To take my mind off my current break-up Zak convinced me to join an Improv class with him.

In today's class the teacher paired Zak and Asia (a woman who earlier announced she was pregnant) for a game of Shout It Out, an improv game in which 2 people go on-stage and the crowd yells random scenarios for the 2 to act out.

A classmate yelled "gang fight!"

And Zak. Well, Zak yelled the first thing that came out of his stupid mouth,

"I'm gonna give you an abortion with my fist!"

She started to cry but Zak thought she was acting so he continued to throw fake jabs into the air.

The class was dead silent as she ran from the room balling.

Our teacher said you can never take improv too far, "but Zak took it too far."

At least instead of crying over some dumb boy, I'm laughing at Zak.

—#CancelZak Journal

HEALING FROM THE HURT

Finding love for another human is like finding new meaning in life. When that love is lost, we feel as if we lost meaning in our lives.

Real healing begins with self-love. No person, place, or thing is responsible for your happiness but yourself. Find closure with the apology that won't come. When you hold on to the past or past lover, you prohibit your life from moving in any direction except backward.

It's not easy living in this "new world" without the person you loved most but the grief you are experiencing is not so much about the past, but about the mourning of the future you thought you had. With healing, it takes time and more importantly, **you-time.**

Healing takes strength. Resist the urge to stalk them via social media. If it's hurting the healing process, block them (out of sight, out of mind). Knowing when to leave is important; the job. The party. The relationship. You'll learn.

With healing, this is the time where **bad emotions are good emotions.** Use those emotions of detest, depression, and despair as training tools to remember how hurt you were so you can move on and never feel that way again. If they or you try to reenter that past bubble, remind yourself of those emotions won't go away. A negative emotion that's actually positive: greed. Be greedy when it comes to your needs. We overthink, over-trust, over-love, and over-cared for everyone but ourselves— *start thinking, trusting, loving, and caring about yourself.*

We wish there was magic advice getting over an ex. **But time time time.** You will heal. Don't let one shitty day determine your week and don't let one shitty relationship determine your love life.

Many people are terrified of healing because their identity is centered around the trauma they've faced. Sometimes we are trauma-bond to a pattern because of the strange comfort in it. Trauma from any major event doesn't define you. You are <u>not</u> responsible for your trauma, but you <u>are</u> responsible for healing.

Taking the power back comes with two options: evolve or repeat.

Repeat is when you keep putting yourself in a toxic situation. You keep entering an unhealthy environment on a nonstop emotional rollercoaster expecting change. But it doesn't make you an idiot to repeat— *you're human.* Trial and error is a part of the process. Sometimes when you repeat so much, you *evolve*.

Evolve isn't something drastic like moving across the country or murdering your ex. It's simple. Stop texting them back or simply giving less of a fuck. Give up the need to be in situations that are draining your energy. Real self-care isn't a shopping spree or spa day (which helps) but it's those difficult conversations with oneself to set boundaries and rules.

As we heal and drive toward closure, whether closure from a person or an event, realize that closure is dependent on you. If you are waiting for that closure to be received from anyone but yourself, you'll be waiting forever.

It's tough.

I played 101 scenarios to what I would say to my ex. And I did this next exercise because I realized my ex would never give me the closure I needed.

Write a letter to the person or event you want closure from— spill your fucking heart out:

_____

_____

_____

_____

_____

_____

_____

_____

_____

_____

_____

_____

_____

_____

_____

_____

_____

_____

_____

_____

_____

_____

_____

_____Goodbye.

When trying to move on, my therapist asked something that never left my brain, "what does moving on look like to you?"

What does moving on look like to you?

_____

_____

_____

_____

_____

_____

_____

_____

_____

_____

**MOVING ON IS A LONELY JOURNEY,
DON'T FALL BACKWARD WHEN THEY
TRY WEASELING THEIR WAY BACK
INTO YOUR LIFE:**

spend time with yourself, give all
that misguided love to yourself.

life will become more boring as you
detach from the drama and that's okay,
attach to the monotony of a drama-less
life.

let go of that first impression of them
— people change.

accept that life goes on.

find peace with the closure you will
never get.

recognize if the person you can't
move on from has more to do with the
fact that you couldn't cope with the
rejection of them not wanting you and
less with you actually liking them.

Remember, new results take a new formula.

Dear Journal, it's Zak.

I accidentally told my therapist I was going to kill myself.

I don't think he understands my dark humor. He just looked at me like I was going to do get up and jump out the window.

I hate being depressed AND having dark humor... if I was going to kill myself, I wouldn't waste my time in therapy. I'd probably go skydiving and "forget" my backpack.

—I'M KIDDING Journal, laugh, I'm funny.

YOU ARE NOT FUCKING ALONE

When rejection or "the Zakar Curse" occurs, we tend to think we are the only people in the world going through *that* problem. There's some comfort in knowing that everyone's fucking up because you are not fucking alone.

We repeat **you. are. not. fucking. alone.**

Feeling alone is another example of how losing your initial focus causes a chain reaction of problems. Unfocused on happiness, with an intense focus on loneliness and you'll fall into depression.

Depression is a ticking time bomb. There is no comfort in depression, it's unrecognizable. That's why when you're sad "no one understands" what you're going through but we all understand because you're not fucking alone.

Loneliness will tell you your friends are suddenly abandoning you and your family suddenly couldn't give a fuck about you.

Enjoy the alone time. Within your alone time, you will become reckless, you'll sleep around, you'll make regrettable choices, feel insecure, be triggered by Ariana Grande because your ex loved her— it's normal. This time is for you to grow, learn and understand yourself. You finally have the power to do whatever the fuck you want— *fewer attachments, maybe Buddha was on to something.*

In overcoming loneliness, you will undergo every emotion under the fucking rainbow: love, hate, excitement, sadness, and most importantly, forgiveness. Until you get comfortable with being alone, you'll never know if you're choosing someone or something out of love or loneliness. Learn to forgiver yourself like you did your ex so many times. After some time, your confidence will come back. You'll rebuild yourself and hold on to your best qualities.

"Let the past make you better, not bitter."
-Buddha

Finish the poem with your best qualities.

Roses are red, Violets are blue:

_____

_____

_____

_____

_____

_____

_____

Constant reminder to love yourself.

Dear Journal, it's Michael.

Tonight, I found my next boyfriend.
I went over to his house for a three-sum with
his friend. I've had 2 other three-sums prior and
walked out both times because I was too
uncomfortable... third time's a charm!
When I arrived at this man's apartment, the
third person was running late. In the meantime,
he ended up making me spaghetti while we
waited for our third. In those two hours, we
talked about our entire lives. We connected.
Conversation never spilled so quickly.
The third came but the three-sum never
happened because I had to go home early. Or at
least that's what we told the third so he would
leave.
Me and Mr. Spaghetti Man ended up having sex
because we were so into each other.

...

3 years later I was right about this connection.
Every anniversary we eat spaghetti.
Love always happens when you least expect it.

—Take care, Journal

YOU'RE HOT BUT ARE YOU GOOD FOR MY MENTAL HEALTH?

When moving on remember to give this next person a fair try. **They are not your ex** and you will repeat the same trauma if continue to see every suitor this way.

Putting yourself out there can tricky. Don't open your legs for someone who calls you pretty (like Zak). Settling is not moving on.

Lower those expectations. If they're amazing over Bumble, they may suck in person. Not every person you meet will be Prince Charming.

And this lesson took me years of shitty relationships to figure out: people want to date the authentic version of you. I'd always try too hard for potential lovers when all I had to do was less. Crazy to think being yourself attracts more people.

"True love is born from understanding."
-Buddha

**Circle 3 words that are the most important
to you in a lover:**

Caring. Happy. Giving. Idealistic. Emotional.

Independent. Friendly. Weird. Supportive.

Funny. Smart. Spontaneous. Passionate.

Trust-worthy. Experienced. Vulnerable.

Animated. Social. Deep. Persistent. Deep.

Daring. Respectful. Patient. Faithful.

Surprise!

You are what you're looking for in others. Look at the words you've circled— *your lover is someone like* *you*.

What do you want in your next relationship?

_____

_____

_____

_____

_____

_____

_____

_____

_____

_____

For readers in a relationship, why have you stayed? Is there anything you would like to change about your current relationship?

_____

_____

_____

_____

_____

_____

_____

_____

_____

_____

_____

_____

Having a healthy balance of mental and physical chemistry is important, what does sex mean to you?

_____

_____

_____

_____

_____

_____

_____

_____

_____

We leave you with this last piece of love advice: love when you're ready, not when you're lonely.

SURROUND YOURSELF WITH MARTINIS NOT FUCKS

Dear Journal, it's Michael.

Sometimes I like my awkwardness.
Today at my friend's dad's funeral I hugged my friend's Muslim friend.
As soon as I did everyone in the room gasped.
Someone yelled,
"She can't hug boys!"
Apparently in Islamic law, females are not supposed to make physical contact with the opposite gender.
I immediately apologized and awkwardly went in for another hug...
Maybe not the right time, but I make myself laugh.

—Facepalm Journal

10'S ACROSS THE BOARD

Write 10 things you like about yourself. You could write about the time you defended a friend. Or that time you didn't kill Karen (write something meaningful):

1.＿＿＿＿＿＿＿＿＿＿＿＿＿＿＿＿＿＿

＿＿＿＿＿＿＿＿＿＿＿＿＿＿＿＿＿＿＿

＿＿＿＿＿＿＿＿＿＿＿＿＿＿＿＿＿＿＿

2.＿＿＿＿＿＿＿＿＿＿＿＿＿＿＿＿＿＿

＿＿＿＿＿＿＿＿＿＿＿＿＿＿＿＿＿＿＿

＿＿＿＿＿＿＿＿＿＿＿＿＿＿＿＿＿＿＿

3.＿＿＿＿＿＿＿＿＿＿＿＿＿＿＿＿＿＿

＿＿＿＿＿＿＿＿＿＿＿＿＿＿＿＿＿＿＿

＿＿＿＿＿＿＿＿＿＿＿＿＿＿＿＿＿＿＿

4.＿＿＿＿＿＿＿＿＿＿＿＿＿＿＿＿＿＿

＿＿＿＿＿＿＿＿＿＿＿＿＿＿＿＿＿＿＿

＿＿＿＿＿＿＿＿＿＿＿＿＿＿＿＿＿＿＿

5.＿＿＿＿＿＿＿＿＿＿＿＿＿＿＿＿＿＿

＿＿＿＿＿＿＿＿＿＿＿＿＿＿＿＿＿＿＿

6._____

7._____

8._____

9._____

10._____

Done?

We asked you to complete this list because if you're ever having a rough day, look at this list to remind yourself of your positive qualities.

This list is who you embody. And hey, if you couldn't think of 10, now's the time to start working on reasons to love yourself!

We'll give you one: it's admirable that you want to work on being happy. That makes you someone whose worthy of friendship and love.

So from two humans to another, give yourself some fucking credit. The hardest thing in this world is living in it. The world is better with you in it. You fail to realize the impact you have or will have on people.

THE SUNFLOWER

The story you're about to read is one of the things I wrote on my top 10 list of things I like about myself.

Dear Journal, it's Zak.

It's the summer of 2016 and I scored the worst fucking one-day side gig pouring champagne for rich white people outside a boujie restaurant in downtown Detroit.

When the event started, I got the impression my one-day boss was a complete cunt... I was right.

Earlier in the day, I was asked to put sunflower arrangements on the tables of the restaurant. Once completed, I returned outside to pour champagne.

Two hours later, I was asked to clear the arrangements from each table. As I am doing so a girl with down-syndrome approaches me and asks if she could have a sunflower because they were her favorite flower.

Before I could answer, my cunty boss grabs the arrangements,

"The flowers are for display only."

She then openly throws away 24 sunflowers right before her eyes.

The girl looked crushed.

Shortly after, I went back to pouring champagne. That's when this overly-joyed drunk woman stumbles over to me for a refill,

"Damn, I'm so drunk, my pussy is falling out."

Being the token gay of the employees, I try making her feel better with my awkward humor,

"Girl, it's all good. My pussy's falling out too."

Before I know it, the cunty boss pulls me aside in a furious rage,

"Why are you talking about that girl's pussy? She's the manager's daughter."

I try defusing the situation,

"I wasn't talking about her vagina. I was talking about my theoretic vagina."

She didn't understand gay lingo and fired me on the spot for sexual harassment. I was still getting paid for the event so I was more than pumped to get out of this lady's negative web early.

I decide to steal a bottle of champagne. On my way out, I notice the girl with down syndrome having dinner with her family and see balloons surrounding her table. It was her 14th birthday.

I run to the kitchen trash.

"Have an amazing birthday," I say, dropping two dozen sunflowers on the table.

She cried tears of joy.

Now when people ask what my favorite flower is I say sunflower because it's a flower attributed to a moment of happiness I gave someone.

A pro-tip for humans, happiness starts with action. This lesson taught me what true happiness is: connection— Whether that connection is to yourself or another human. If you can go out of your way to make someone happy for a couple of seconds, you'll indirectly make yourself happy. Sparking other people's flames will cause a bigger fire in your soul.

When I think back on "who I want to be," I go back to this day. I want to be that guy who made that girl's day a little bit better with a simple action.

—Sorry for rambling Journal,
 I know I sound like Mother
 Theresa.

Dear Journal, it's Zak.

I never understood the mind of a murderer until I went into business with my twin.

Today, we are in San Francisco about halfway done with the drag queen tour. Tensions were high on the bus but thank God we got a hotel tonight.

The thing with twins is when one gets stressed from any outside source they take it out on the other twin. So Michael's bitch ass was ready to attack me the moment I said something stupid and I ALWAYS say something stupid. Not really sure how it started but I was eating this banana on my side of the room and Michael starts yelling at me for existing?

As a result, I ended up throwing my banana at his head. He then took the banana and threw it back at me. This spiraled into a screaming match about our insecurities as we keep throwing banana mush back and forth at each other.

The room was wrecked rock band style with banana everywhere. What could have been a relaxing day was ruined because we both don't know when to shut the fuck up.

I don't have anger issues— I have Michael issues.

> —Seriously Journal, should I listen
> to my inner Pisces and murder
> him?

THE LAST WORD

On this journey of happiness, you'll be working on finding yourself. You'll begin to point out and working on your flaws. In doing so, you'll naturally become more defensive. Let's talk having the last word, you argumentative bitch.

For so long when someone argued with us, we went in full defensive mode as we felt we were being criticized. The ego can confuse someone giving you "tough love" as "being attacked." At the end of the day, you don't have to take their advice. If you find yourself feeling defensive it's because there's some truth to what's being said. If it's an attack tell them to "fuck off" and keep moving.

Recognize the difference between creative criticism and destructive criticism. Creative criticism stems from a good place. Destructive criticism comes from a bad place. If it's not conversational, it's destructive.

Arguing isn't about being right or wrong (but it's ok to be wrong). Your peace is more important than proving your point. We learned to take what people said about us, reflect on it and change if we felt this critique resonated.

Think of your words as a bottle of toothpaste. Squeeze it. Now if we ask you to put that toothpaste back into its tube, you would see how difficult it may be.

Your words hold the ability to brighten or destroy someone's (or your own) day. Regret comes from squeezing too hard.

Be our own biggest critic and self-reflect:
What/where do you think you need fixing?
(I realized I needed to speak up. I was a loudmouth
who censored my real feelings to compensate
for others, now I don't shut up.)

_____

_____

_____

_____

_____

_____

_____

_____

_____

_____

I'M CONFIDENT
MY LAST WORDS
WILL BE,
"ARE YOU
FUCKING
KIDDING ME?"

Dear Journal, it's Michael.

If you want to see the ugliest side of the human race, try watching someone make content for social media.

I would like social media more if I wasn't an "influencer." It's as impressive as telling someone you have an Associates's Degree (I have 3.)

Every day I have to act and perform happy even if I don't feel like it. And taking selfies with Zak takes forever. It's a truly draining process (we have lost friends this way.) We can never agree on a picture that flatters us both and end up calling each other names.

This afternoon Zak and I had to take pictures in these sponsored shirts.

Zak scrolled through the phone a dozen times asking why my face looked like "that." To which I screamed, "that's just my fucking face!"

We got into a screaming match that ended in tears but we got a bomb ass selfie.

—G2G, Journal

#HOWTOBEFUCKINGHAPPY

There are two places you should never stay too long: in your head and on social media.

We are humans who strive to connect. Connection is what makes this world livable. To master the power of connection, let's start with a little exercise, shall we?

Text 5 people: "hey, thinking about you. Hope you're okay!"

Who comes to mind? If one's an ex, we'll slap you.

Yes, social media is an amazing place to connect. We made an entire career out of it. But let's discuss the cons of social media and what to watch out for.

As toxic as social media is, it's not going anywhere. Realistically, you'll need to be on social media to keep up in the modern world and it's about finding a happy medium.

Social media is a world of smoke and mirrors. It gives us the power to be whoever we want. A chance to brag to the world that we live luxurious lives. We're able to escape from the hardships of reality as we edit, crop, and fix the imperfections of our lives.

Make social media your bitch. If you're going to allow yourself to spend endless hours of the day on the internet, learn to connect your goals in the process. Start an online business, use the infinite knowledge of Google to start a craft, use Tinder to find a new lover— scroll with purpose.

Learn the power of disconnecting. Learning this ability is dangerous because if you do it too well, you'll become closed-off from both the social media world and the real world. This power comes from within to shut certain emotions off. With disconnect, we allow ourselves to make choices not ridden with a second thought.

The best moments in life are those not spent on the phone. We never realized how powerful it was to disconnect from the virtual world. The idea that no one in the world knew where the fuck we were or what the fuck we were doing was freeing.

List 3 of what you'd like to fix, do, or limit on social media.

1._____

_____

_____

2._____

_____

_____

3._____

_____

_____

Go into your phone settings and put on Screen Time so you can monitor and manage how much time you're putting into your phone.

Dear Journal, it's Michael.

I need a new therapist.

Today, I confessed to myself that sometimes I feel invisible compared to my introverted twin.

As I walked out... she called me Zak.

I hate being a twin... and yes, I cried in the elevator.

—I'M MICHAEL, Journal!

SHIT MY THERAPIST SAYS

People go to therapy to deal with the people that **need** to go to therapy.

Before we went to therapy, there was resistance because we wanted to remain "strong." We assumed that therapy was for the weak-minded. Strengthening your mind is not crazy, therapy is school for the brain.

Why wouldn't you protect the most important organ in your body?

We, as humans, need a logical voice of reason. Friends are great, but they're biased. I went to therapy cause I struggled with intrusive thoughts. Intrusive thoughts are thoughts that manifest and bloom poorly into our brains (if you deal with intrusive thoughts, go to therapy. Minor problems in our lives can cause major turmoil).

Intrusive thoughts cause turmoil because they come out of nowhere. Intrusive thoughts are built on sexual, violent, or socially unacceptable images and bring major anxiety to individuals because they fear that they might commit the acts they picture or think this means something terrible about them could emerge in the future— this is not true because the future doesn't exist and you are being bombarded by repetitive thoughts.

But of course, when one tries to get "rid" of these thoughts, the thought intensifies. People dealing with intrusive thoughts need to realize that these thoughts are that— *intrusive. They are in no way relevant.* Most of what you fear is inside your head. Intrusive thoughts feed on your lack of confidence.

```
DEALNG WITH INTRUSIVE
THOUGHTS CONSISTS OF

attempting to figure out what they mean,
but don't engage in any way.

allowing time to pass.

continuing whatever you were doing prior
to the thoughts.

remembering who you are.
(you're that bitch. Been that bitch, still that
bitch, you will forever be that bitch)

looking for guidance.
(some community centers, hospitals,
schools and places of worship offer free
counseling)
```

Now let's talk therapy.

Picking a therapist is like picking friends— some may feel right, some may feel wrong. You need someone who understands your struggles. If you're struggling with your sexual identity, a queer therapist is where you'd want to lean. Or if you're a woman struggling with the constant sexism in the world, lean toward a female therapist. You'll most likely shuffle through a few to find the right one.

There are dozens of different types of therapy, so explore what works for you.

Let's talk about a Zakar Twins favorite, art therapy. For me, Michael, art is a way to get away from the world for just a mental minute because sometimes I just don't feel like talking. Complete focus to create art.

Let's try it.

Draw a happy person:

Not really sure what you drew... looks like a dog. Time to take an art class.

Write the best piece of advice you've ever been given:

_____

_____

_____

_____

_____

_____

_____

_____

_____

_____

Use the power of social media and share this advice with others. Trust us when we say someone needs to hear it! Hashtag it *#HowToBeFuckingHappy #HTBFH*

Dear Journal, it's Zak.

It only took a fucking year, but I'm starting to find my people!
I feel like after the break-up I lost half my friends because they were more my ex's friends.
But tonight, I made a new friend! He was dressed as a unicorn at some Halloween party.
Finally, a new gay friend that's not Michael.

—Alright Journal, I have to get ready for my new friend date.

LIFE IS A JOKE GOD IS CONSTANTLY WRITING

Life is fucking strange.

There are no guidelines or rules on how you must live life. You're free to choose any version. This lesson was made prevalent when I was hanging out with a new friend, James.

James was very spiritual. He was always telling me to manifest, meditate, or do shit I wasn't familiar with.

I felt myself becoming more spiritually and less religious over the years, so having a new spiritual friend was a nice shift from my lovable but toxic friends.

One night, we got tipsy and James told me a story about a spiritual awakening he had had. Like any good awakening, this story started one summer at the Coachella music festival while he was on acid...

Upon arrival, James meets a friendly stranger who lets him pick from a pile of stickers in her backpack. He pulled out a unicorn sticker, had a pleasant conversation with her, and was on his way.

Later on that day, he engaged in a wild game of rock, paper, scissors with another vendor. The winner was able to take something from the other. Kind of weird but I don't judge festival kids.

But James won! His eyes looked around the stand when he saw something calling to him: a beaded unicorn necklace.

Finally, when the acid was in full effect, he started vibin' with one of the bands on the main stage. He closed his eyes, felt the music, and wept. He described this overwhelming feeling of love.

When James opened his eyes, the same girl who gave him the unicorn sticker was staring back at him.

She looked at him bewildered,

"Dude, I don't know how I got here, but the universe must have placed me here to give you a hug."

It was in that embrace he was convinced a unicorn was his spirit animal. A unicorn became his reminder to push forward when things got hard. A symbol of happiness.

It was truly a beautiful story. But at the same time, I realized something at that moment— I'll never be that deep. And this is something I was completely okay with.

I wanted so badly for there to be some sort of deeper meaning in life and this unicorn story showed me life's meaning is what you give it.

Life isn't that deep and for some it is. Life gets hard and you may ask yourself where your place is in the world. There's a purpose for you in this world, but you have to explore it. So live and be happy with the craziness you create, because the rarest unicorn is you.

....

Well 🦄 — *we're at the end of today's episode.*

Remember just because this journal ends doesn't mean your journey does.

Reflect.
After reading this how do you feel?
Did this journal help?

_____

_____

_____

_____

_____

_____

_____

_____

_____

_____

_____

_____

_____

CONNECT WITH THE AUTHORS

Photography: Erin McConnell//MUA: Nico Cortes

Follow our journey @ZakarTwins

If you want to hear more about our story purchase, *Pray the Gay Away*, on Amazon.com. Stay happy, womb-mates xx.

Printed in the United States of America
First Edition
ISBN: 978-0-578-93737-3

Cover Art: @Yozart

We hope this book helped in some way.
If it did, give it an Amazon review or post your
reflection page.

Made in the USA
Coppell, TX
22 July 2021

59340030R00088